DreamWorks

DRAGONS

1001
THINGS TO FIND

igloo books

Can you find 1001 dragon items?

Welcome to the exciting island of Berk.
Follow the Dragon Riders around and look out for
the Whispering Death and Screaming Death hidden
on every page. Once you've found them, see if
you can find the other hidden items as well.

Whispering Death　　　　　　　**Screaming Death**

Let's have a practice. Can you see the Whispering Death
and Screaming Death on the page opposite? Once you've
spotted them, try and find these items as well.

4 Boats　　　　　　　　　**5 Baby Gronckles**

7
aby Nightmares

8
Shields

9
Guards

10
Chickens

20
Piles of Dragon Poop

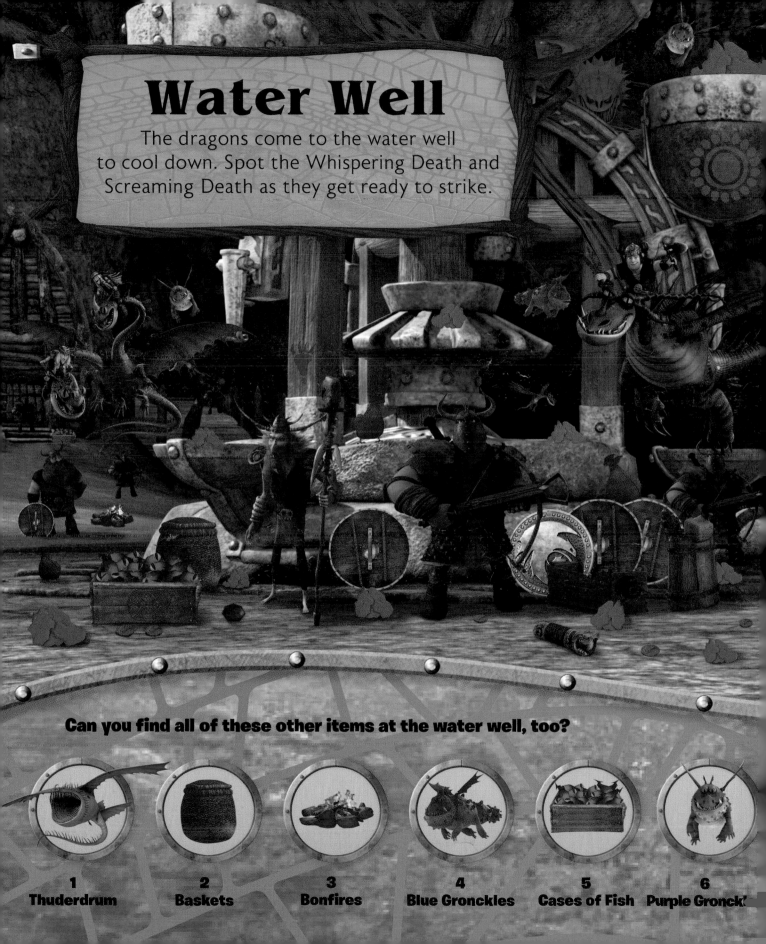

Water Well

The dragons come to the water well to cool down. Spot the Whispering Death and Screaming Death as they get ready to strike.

Can you find all of these other items at the water well, too?

1 Thuderdrum

2 Baskets

3 Bonfires

4 Blue Gronckles

5 Cases of Fish

6 Purple Gronck'

See if you can spot these things at the arena, too.

1 Sword in Shield

2 Chests

3 Barrels

4 Red Shields

5 Axes

6 Scythes

7 Blue Shields

8 Swords

9 Lanterns

10 Helmets

20 Black Crystals

Amazing Arena

It's training time. Quick! Try to spot the Whispering Death and Screaming Death before they cause chaos at the arena.

7
Rocks

8
Shields

9
Maces

10
Swords

20
Stinky Fish

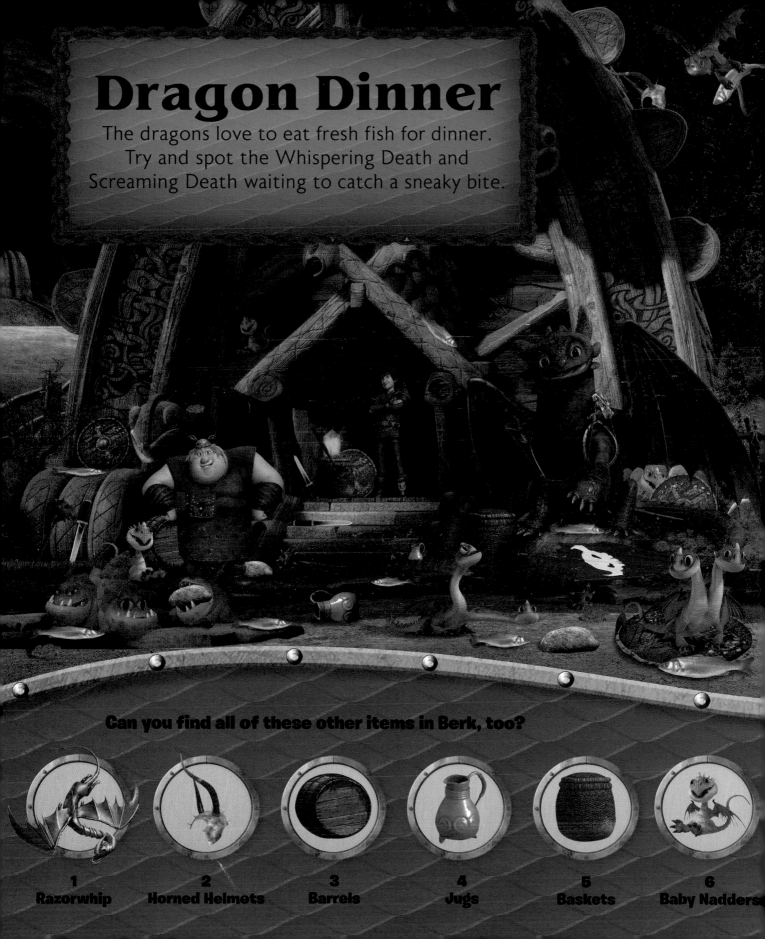

See if you can spot these things in the village, too.

1 Death Song

2 Barrels

3 Piles of Sacks

4 Sheep

5 Shields

6 Teeth

7 Stinky Fish

8 Baby Zipplebacks

9 Swords

10 Helmets

20 Eggs

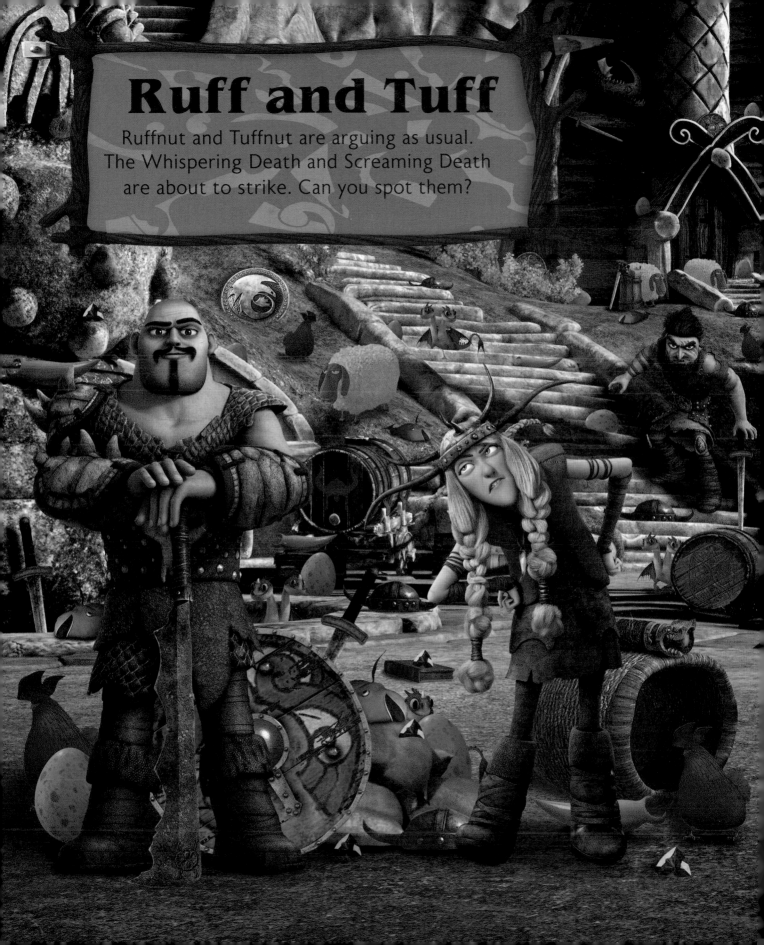

Ruff and Tuff

Ruffnut and Tuffnut are arguing as usual. The Whispering Death and Screaming Death are about to strike. Can you spot them?

See if you can spot these things at the cliffs, too.

1 Shield **2 Maces**

3 Baby Gronckles **4 Baby Nightmares**

5 Axes **6 Baby Nadders**

7 Baby Zipplebacks **8 Dragon Roots**

9 Toadstools **10 Eggs**

20 Emeralds

Egg-cellent

Baby dragons fill the village of Berk.
The Whispering Death and Screaming Death are
about to cause trouble. Can you spot them?

7
Frosty Trees

8
Sheep

9
Shields

10
Baby Nightmares

20
Icicles

Freeze Finds

Snow has covered the village of Berk.
Spot the Whispering Death and
Screaming Death hidden in this wintry scene.

Can you find all of these other items in Berk, too?

1
Crate of Dragons

2
Statues

3
Yaks

4
Stools

5
Fire Pits

6
Baby Zippleback

See if you can spot these things in the Scene, too.

1 Thunderdrum

2 Night Fury Shields

3 Yaks

4 Night Terrors

5 Gronckles

6 Deadly Nadder

7 Shields

8 Terrible Terrors

9 Hookfang Shields

10 Sheep

20 Sacks

Brilliant Berk

The Whispering Death and Screaming Death
are lurking somewhere in this busy flying scene
around Berk. Can you spot them?

7
Swords

8
Sheep

9
Apples

10
Helmets

20
Leaves

Forest Finds

The forests around Berk are great places for dragons to hide. Can you find the Whispering Death and Screaming Death?

Can you find all of these other items in the forest, too?

1
Baby Nightmare

2
Axes

3
Baby Gronckles

4
Barrels

5
Terrible Terrors

6
Shields

1 Night Fury

2 Chests

3 Baskets

4 Axes

5 Shields

6 Chickens

7 Rocks

8 Terrible Terrors

9 Baby Nightmares

10 Jugs

20 Helmets

Busy Berk

The village of Berk is always busy with
people working hard to keep the island safe.
Can you find the special hidden dragons?